Bertha's Secret Battle

Yr 3
T/I.

Dramatised from
John Coldwell's story
by David Calcutt

Illustrated by Doffy Weir

Oxford University Press

Oxford University Press, Great Clarendon Street, Oxford OX2 6DP

Oxford   New York
Athens   Auckland   Bangkok   Bogota   Buenos Aires
Calcutta   Cape Town   Chennai   Dar es Salaam
Delhi   Florence   Hong Kong   Istanbul   Karachi
Kuala Lumpur   Madrid   Melbourne   Mexico City
Mumbai   Nairobi   Paris   São Paulo   Singapore
Taipei   Tokyo   Toronto   Warsaw

and associated companies in
Berlin   Ibadan

Oxford is a registered trade mark of Oxford University Press

© David Calcutt 1998
First published 1998

Adapted from the novel **Bertha's Secret Battle**
by John Coldwell, published by Oxford University
Press in 1995.

ISBN 0 19 918786 X

Printed in Hong Kong

Cast list

There are twelve parts in this play,
but you can act it out with a cast of
six, if some actors take two parts and
some actors take three.

Bertha

Fiona

Referee / Helen / Manager

Audience 1 / Tom / Shopper

Audience 2 / Mr Wiggins

Audience 3 / Mrs Twiggins

Scene 1

*The wrestling ring at the
Town Hall.* **Bertha** *enters from
one side, and* **Fiona** *from the
other. They are both wearing
dressing-gowns.* **Bertha** *has
a red wig, and* **Fiona** *has a
blonde wig.*

Bertha   I'm Bertha.

Fiona   I'm Fiona.

Bertha   We're sisters.

Fiona	Twin sisters.
Bertha	There's only one way to tell us apart.
Fiona	I dye my hair blonde.
Bertha	And I dye my hair red.
Fiona	And every Friday night we go to the Town Hall.
Bertha	And we wrestle.
Fiona	Because that's what we are.
Bertha	Wrestlers.

*The **referee** enters and stands in the centre of the ring. Three others enter as the **audience**, and stand around the sides, watching.*

Referee   Ladies and gentlemen! Tonight's wrestling match is about to begin. First of all, here she is, the darling of the ring. Fairplay Fiona!

Fiona takes off her dressing-gown. She's wearing a pink leotard. She holds her hands above her head and parades around the ring as the **audience** cheer and call out.

All   Hooray!

Audience 1   We love Fiona!

Audience 2	She's our favourite!
Audience 3	Fiona forever!
All	Hooray!

Fiona goes and stands in her corner.

Referee	And now, stand back everyone, here comes her sister. Big Bertha the Bone-Cruncher!

Bertha takes off her dressing-gown. She is wearing a black leotard. She holds her hands above her head and parades around the ring, as the audience boo and call out.

All   Boo!

Audience 1   We hate Bertha!

Audience 2   She's a bad one!

Audience 3   Down with Big Bertha!

All   Boo!

Bertha shakes her fist at the audience. They boo even louder.

All	Booooo!
Referee	All right, that's enough. Come and shake hands, girls.

Bertha and Fiona come to the centre and shake hands. The referee steps back.

Referee	Let the fight begin!
Fiona	And then we fight.
Bertha	Just the way we planned it.

A bell rings. Fiona and Bertha face each other. They don't fight, but instead they describe what happens, while the audience and the referee act as if they can see the fight.

Fiona	First, Bertha throws me against the ropes.
Audience 1	*(Horrified)* She's thrown her against the ropes!

All	Boo!
Bertha	Then Fiona bounces back with a shoulder-charge!
Audience 2	*(Admiring)* What a shoulder-charge!
All	Hooray!
Fiona	And Bertha knocks me down!
Audience 3	Get up, Fiona!
All	Boo!
Bertha	But she's back on her feet again!
Audience 1	She's up!
All	Hooray!
Fiona	Then Bertha gets me in a neck-lock!
Audience 2	Oh no! She's got her in a neck-lock!
All	Boo!

Bertha	But she gets *me* in an arm-lock!
Audience 3	Come on, Fiona!
Fiona	And I force her down!

> **Bertha** *slowly lowers herself to the floor, as if being pushed down by Fiona.*

Bertha	And I don't get up!
Fiona	And the referee counts.
Bertha	And the audience counts.

> The **referee** *counts from one to ten. The* **audience** *count with him.*

Referee **All** }	One! Two! Three! Four! Five! Six! Seven! Eight! Nine! Ten!

> The **referee** *speaks by himself.*

Referee	Out for the count!

Referee   And the winner is – Fairplay Fiona!

All   Hooray!

Bertha is lying on the floor. The referee holds up Fiona's hand.

The audience give a final cheer.

The referee drops Fiona's hand, and goes. The audience go as well, speaking to each other as they go.

Audience 1   That was a good match.

Audience 2	It always is.
Audience 3	Especially as Fiona won again.
Audience 2	She always does.

*The **audience** go. **Fiona** and **Bertha** are left onstage, **Bertha** on the floor, **Fiona** standing above her.*

Bertha	And then she helps me up.

***Fiona** holds out her hand and helps **Bertha** up.*

Fiona	Are you all right, Bertha?
Bertha	Of course I am.

***Fiona** and **Bertha** put their dressing-gowns back on.*

Fiona	And we both go home and have a cup of cocoa.

***Fiona** and **Bertha** go.*

Scene 2

*Fiona's and Bertha's living room, later that evening. **Fiona** and **Bertha** come back onstage again. They are both still wearing their dressing-gowns, but each now carries a cup. They sit down and sip their cocoa.*

Fiona   I thought the fight went very well this evening.

Bertha   *(Miserably)* Of course it did. It always does.

Fiona   It was just like we planned it.

Bertha   Of course it was! It always is.

Fiona   You're not hurt, are you?

Bertha   No. I never am.

Fiona	You weren't upset by the flying shoulder-charge?
Bertha	No.
Fiona	Nor the arm-lock?
Bertha	No.
Fiona	What's the matter, then?
Bertha	There's nothing the matter!
Fiona	Yes, there is. You're upset. Why are you upset?
Bertha	Do you really want to know?
Fiona	Yes.
Bertha	All right, then. *(She begins to cry.)* I'm upset because people always cheer you, and they always boo me.
Fiona	Of course they do. I'm Fairplay Fiona, and you're Big Bertha the Bone-Cruncher.

Bertha   But I'm fed up of being the one they always boo. I want them to cheer *me* for a change.

Fiona   They can't!

Bertha   Why not?

Fiona   Because you're –

Bertha   *(Interrupting Fiona)* I know. I'm Big Bertha the Bone-Cruncher. But I don't have to be all the time.

Fiona   What do you mean?

Bertha	We could change places. You could be… 'Fearsome Fiona'. And I could be… 'Big-Hearted Bertha'.
Fiona	That's silly. You're so good at being bad.
Bertha	I could teach you how to be bad. And you could teach me how to be good.
Fiona	No. It wouldn't work. What would my fans think? You're bad and I'm good. That's the way it's always been, and that's the way it always will be!

*Fiona goes. **Bertha** speaks to herself, angrily.*

Bertha	Oh, yes! That's the way it always is! Fiona's good, and Bertha's bad. It's all right for her, being the good one. She doesn't know what it's like when everybody hates you. And it's about time she did. In fact, if I can think of a plan, this time next week she'll be the bad one, and I'll be the good one. Then they'll boo her, and cheer me.

***Bertha** goes.*

Scene 3

It's the next week, in the morning. **Fiona** *enters, in her pink tracksuit, jogging. She calls out to Bertha.*

Fiona   Bertha! Are you still in the bathroom? Hurry up, will you? I want to dye my hair for the fight tonight!

Bertha calls from the bathroom.

Bertha   I'm just dyeing mine!

Fiona   Be quick! I've got to go for my jog, and then I've got to open the new supermarket.

Bertha	I'm almost ready!
Fiona	All right, then! I'm just going for a quick run round the garden! Be finished when I get back.
Bertha	I will!

> *Fiona jogs offstage. After a little while, Bertha enters. She wears a blonde wig like Fiona's, and she is carrying a towel and two bottles. One is labelled 'Red Hair Dye' and the other is labelled 'Golden Yellow Hair Dye'.*

Bertha	At last! My hair's blonde, like hers. All week I was thinking of a plan, and at last I came up with it. It was so simple. I've used Fiona's dye on my hair, and now, all I've got to do is pour my red dye into her bottle, and the plan's complete!

> *She pours the contents of her bottle into Fiona's.*

Bertha	There. It's done. I'll just put it down here.
	*She puts the bottle down on a table. Offstage, **Fiona** calls.*
Fiona	I hope you've finished, Bertha!
Bertha	*(To herself)* She's coming back! I'd better hide my hair. I don't want her to find out… just yet.
	*She wraps the towel around her head as **Fiona** enters.*

Fiona   At last. Now I can do mine. And then I can
                go for my jog.

                *She picks up the bottle that
                Bertha has put down and goes
                off.* **Bertha** *grins.*

Bertha   She's about to dye her hair red. And she's in
                such a hurry, she won't even notice. I can't
                wait till tonight! I feel so good, I think I'll go
                and do a bit of gardening.

                Bertha *goes.*

Scene 4

Later that morning, in the park.
*Two children, **Helen** and **Tom**,*
are playing.

Helen	Are you going to the wrestling match at the Town Hall tonight, Tom?
Tom	Of course. I always go.
Helen	And me. Do you think Fiona will win again?
Tom	Of course she will. She always wins.
Helen	We might see her today. She often comes jogging through the park on Fridays.
Tom	I hope so. She's the best.
Helen	She is. But that Big Bertha's horrible.

Tom looks offstage.

Tom	Hey! Helen!
Helen	What?
Tom	I think I can see her.

Helen	Fairplay Fiona? Where?
Tom	There! Jogging along the path.

Helen looks.

Helen	She's coming this way… *(She pauses)* … wait a minute… that's not her…
Tom	It must be. She's wearing pink.
Helen	I know, but look at her hair –
Tom	You're right! It's not her at all. It's… the other one!

Fiona enters, jogging. She has Bertha's red wig on.

Fiona	Hello there, children!

The children cry out in fear.

Tom	Go away!
Helen	Leave us alone!

Tom   We don't like you!

Helen   Help!

                            They run off, scared.
                            Fiona *calls after them.*

Fiona   Where are you going? It's me!
               Fairplay Fiona!

*The **children** have gone.*

Fiona   What's the matter with them?
Why did they run away from me
like that? It was as if I'd scared them!

*A **policeman**
enters, behind her.*

Policeman   What do you think you're doing?

Fiona tries to
speak to him.

Fiona   I –

Policeman   I saw you, frightening those children.

Fiona   But –

Policeman   Don't you know it's against the law to frighten people in the park? You horrible person!

Fiona   But I'm not a horrible person!

Policeman   Yes, you are, and I won't have you in this park. Go on! Get out of it. And don't let me catch you in here again!

*Upset, **Fiona** jogs off. The*
***policeman** is pleased with*
himself.

Policeman   It all makes the job worth doing, when you can keep places safe from people like that. Big Bertha! I can't stand her! And neither can anybody else!

Scene 5

*A little while later. A man and a woman, **Mr Wiggins** and **Mrs Twiggins**, enter with shopping bags. They are standing outside a supermarket.*

Mr Wiggins   Hello, Mrs Twiggins.

Mrs Twiggins   Hello, Mr Wiggins. Have you come for the opening of the new supermarket?

Mr Wiggins   Yes. I heard they've got a famous person to come and open it.

Mrs Twiggins   They have. And do you know who it is? Fairplay Fiona!

Mr Wiggins   Fairplay Fiona? She's coming here?

Mrs Twiggins   Yes. I can't wait to meet her.

Mr Wiggins   She's my favourite.

Mrs Twiggins   And mine. She's so brave, and fearless, and fair!

Mr Wiggins	Not like that Big Bertha.
Mrs Twiggins	No. She's horrible.

*The **supermarket manager**
enters.*

Manager	Hello. I'm the manager of the new supermarket. I'm sorry you've been kept waiting so long. Fairplay Fiona should have been here by now.
Mr Wiggins	It doesn't matter. We don't mind waiting.
Mrs Twiggins	We'd wait all day for Fairplay Fiona.
Manager	I'm sure she'll be here soon.

*Another **shopper** enters.*

Shopper	Are you waiting for Fairplay Fiona?
Manager	Yes. Is she coming?
Shopper	Well, I *thought* she was…
Mr Wiggins	What do you mean?

Mrs Twiggins	Have you seen her?
Shopper	I thought I did. I saw her jogging down the road in her pink tracksuit…
Manager	That's her, all right.
Shopper	But then she came closer, and I saw…
Mr Wiggins	Saw what?
Shopper	It wasn't her!
Mrs Twiggins	If it wasn't her, who was it?

Fiona enters, jogging. She is still wearing Bertha's red wig.

Fiona	Hello, everyone. Sorry I'm a bit late.
Shopper	Her!
Mr Wiggins	Oh, no!
Mrs Twiggins	How horrible!
Mr Wiggins	I'm not staying here!

Mrs Twiggins	Not with her!
Shopper	She'll knock everything off the shelves!
Mr Wiggins	Smash all the eggs!
Mrs Twiggins	Spill the milk all over the floor!

Mrs Twiggins, Mr Wiggins,
*and the **shopper** back away*
from Fiona.

Manager   *(To Fiona)* Now see what you've done! You've
ruined the opening of my new supermarket!

Fiona   But how? I've come to open it.

Manager   We didn't want *you*. And I'm not letting you
into my supermarket! Get away from here!
You're nothing but trouble!

*The **manager** and **shoppers***
go. Fiona is very upset by now.

Fiona   What *is* the matter with everyone today!
Nobody seems to like me! It's terrible! And
that's just how I feel. Terrible!

***Fiona** jogs off.*

Scene 6

*That evening. Fiona and Bertha's garden at home. **Bertha** enters in her black tracksuit. She is doing some gardening and humming happily to herself. She wears Fiona's blonde wig.*

Bertha   I love to do a little gardening before a fight. It really makes me feel relaxed. And this evening, I feel more relaxed than I've ever felt before. Because I know I'm going to win.

Fiona enters, looking very sad.

Bertha   Hello, Fiona. Have a good jog?

Fiona   No.

Bertha   How did the opening of the supermarket go?

Fiona   Terrible.

Bertha   Oh, dear. What a shame.

Fiona   Nobody seemed to like me. Everywhere I went –

*She stops, and suddenly notices
Bertha's hair.*

Fiona   Your hair!

Bertha   What about it?

Fiona   It's… it's *my* hair!

Bertha   Don't be silly, Fiona. It's mine.

Fiona   I mean, it looks like mine! It's my colour!

Bertha   I know. Do you like it?

Fiona   I think it looks better on me.

Bertha	I'm not so sure. I think *my* hair colour looks better on you.
Fiona	What?
Bertha	Look.

She takes out a small mirror and holds it up so that **Fiona** *can see into it.* **Fiona** *gives a cry.*

Fiona	It's red! My hair's red! But that's your colour!
Bertha	No. It's yours now.
Fiona	That's why no one liked me. They thought I was you. How did you do this?

Bertha	Simple. This morning, I dyed my hair with your hair colour, then tipped my hair colour into your empty bottle. When you dyed your hair, you were in such a hurry to get out, you didn't notice.
Fiona	*(Angry)* Very clever. I'll have to go and do my hair all over again, now.
Bertha	You can't.
Fiona	Why not?
Bertha	I tipped the rest of your hair colour down the sink.
Fiona	What! But we're due at the Town Hall in ten minutes! What are we going to do?
Bertha	There's only one thing we can do. You be me, and I'll be you.
Fiona	But –
Bertha	See you in the ring, sister!

> **Bertha** walks offstage one way,
> and **Fiona** walks off another.

Scene 7

*The wrestling ring at the Town Hall again, later that evening. The three **audience members** enter.*

Audience 1   Here we are again, then.

Audience 2   Another wrestling night.

Audience 3   I can't wait for it to start.

Audience 1   And to see that terrible Big Bertha beaten again.

Audience 2   Did you hear about her latest mean trick?

Audience 3   No. What was it?

Audience 2   She went around the town today, pretending to be Fiona.

Audience 1   What an awful thing to do!

Audience 2   Nobody was fooled, though. That red hair of hers gave her away.

Audience 3   Good. I'm going to boo her even louder tonight.

*The **referee** enters and speaks to the audience.*

Referee   Ladies and gentlemen! Quiet please for tonight's top wrestling match. Once again, here she is, the darling of the ring, and everybody's favourite – in the red corner, Fairplay Fiona!

***Bertha** comes onstage, wearing Fiona's pink leotard and Fiona's blonde wig. She raises her hands. The audience think she's Fiona, and cheer.*

All   Hooray!

Audience 1   We love Fiona!

Audience 2   She's our favourite!

Audience 3   Fiona forever!

All   Hooray!

***Bertha** goes and stands in her corner.*

Referee	And now, stand well back, because here she comes, in the blue corner, that monster of the ring, Big Bertha the Bone-Cruncher!

*Fiona comes onstage, in Bertha's black leotard, and wearing Bertha's red wig. She holds her hands above her head and parades around the ring. The **audience** think she's Bertha, and boo.*

All	Boo!

Audience 1	We hate Bertha!

Audience 2	She's a bad one!

Audience 3	Down with Big Bertha!

All	Boo!

Referee	All right, that's enough. Come and shake hands, girls.

*Bertha holds her hand out to Fiona, but **Fiona** won't take it.*

Audience 1   Did you see that?

Audience 2   She wouldn't shake hands with Fiona!

Audience 3   She's really mean.

*The **referee** speaks to Fiona and Bertha.*

Referee   Are you ready? *(They both nod.)* Then let the fight begin!

*A bell rings. **Fiona** and **Bertha** face each other. They grab hold of each other's shoulders. The **audience** call out while **Bertha** and **Fiona** speak to each other.*

Audience 1	Come on, Fiona!
Bertha	*(To Fiona)* How do you like being the bad one?
Audience 2	Down with Big Bertha!
Fiona	*(To Bertha)* I don't. Everybody wants me to lose!
Audience 3	Throw her down, Fiona!
Bertha	*(To Fiona)* Now you know how I feel.

*The **audience** call together.*

All	Throw her down! Throw her down! Throw her down!
Bertha	*(To Fiona)* They want me to throw you, so I better had.
Fiona	But –
Bertha	Get ready, here goes.

Bertha takes hold of Fiona's shoulders. Very slowly, she pushes her down to the floor as the audience cheer.

Audience 1   She's down!

Audience 2   And she's not getting up!

The referee counts from one to ten. The audience count with him.

| Referee | One! Two! Three! Four! Five! Six! Seven! |
| All | Eight! Nine! Ten! |

Referee   Out for the count!

> *The **referee** holds up Bertha's hand.*

And the winner is – Fairplay Fiona!

> *The **referee** drops Bertha's hand, and goes. The **audience** go as well, speaking to each other as they go.*

Audience 1   That was a good match.

Audience 2   It always is.

Audience 3   Especially as Fiona won again.

Audience 2   She always does.

> *The **audience** go. **Fiona** and **Bertha** are left onstage, **Fiona** on the floor, **Bertha** standing above her.*

Bertha takes Fiona's hand and helps her up.

Bertha   Well, Fiona? How does it feel to lose?

Fiona   I didn't lose.

Bertha   Yes, you did. I threw you down –

Fiona   But the referee said the winner was Fairplay Fiona, and that's me!

*One of the **audience** comes back on with a bunch of flowers.*

Audience 1   I've brought some flowers for Fiona.

***Fiona** turns to him.*

Fiona   How kind.

He walks past Fiona and gives them to Bertha.

Audience 1   Here you are. I'd just like to say…
you're my favourite wrestler.

Bertha takes the flowers.

Bertha	Thank you.
	He's embarrassed. He turns and goes, quickly.
Fiona	He said those flowers were for me!
Bertha	But he gave them to me!
Fiona	This is ridiculous!

Bertha   I agree. And I've thought of a plan that should keep us both happy.

Fiona   Go on, then. Let's hear it.

Bertha   Every Friday we'll toss a coin, to see which of us dyes their hair red and which one dyes it blonde.

Fiona   No. I won't agree to that.

Bertha   In that case, I'll keep my hair blonde. Then we'll both be Fairplay Fiona. The crowd won't want to see two Fionas fighting. So we won't get paid. And then we'll have to sell our house –

Fiona   All right! I agree.

Bertha   Shake on it?

Fiona   Shake.

                They shake hands, then turn
                and speak to the audience.

Bertha   So that's what we do.

Fiona   Every Friday, before the match, we toss a coin.

                ***Bertha** takes out a coin and*
                tosses it.

Bertha	And sometimes I've got blonde hair and she's got red hair.
Fiona	And sometimes I've got blonde hair… *(She takes the blonde wig off Bertha's head)…* and she's got red hair. *(She puts the red wig on Bertha's head, and the blonde wig on her own.)*
Bertha	And sometimes people cheer me, and I get to win.
Fiona	So we're both happy.
Bertha	And nobody ever knows the difference.

They shake hands again, and go.

The End

Treetops Playscripts
Titles in the series include:

Stage 10
The Masked Cleaning Ladies of Om
by John Coldwell; adapted
by David Calcutt
  single: 0 19 918780 0
  pack of 6: 0 19 918781 9

Stupid Trousers
by Susan Gates; adapted by David Calcutt
  single: 0 19 918782 7
  pack of 6: 0 19 918783 5

Stage 11
Bertha's Secret Battle
by John Coldwell; adapted
by David Calcutt
  single: 0 19 918786 X
  pack of 6: 0 19 918787 8

Bertie Wiggins' Amazing Ears
by David Cox and Erica James; adapted
by David Calcutt
  single: 0 19 918784 3
  pack of 6: 0 19 918785 1

Stage 12
The Lie Detector
by Susan Gates; adapted by David Calcutt
  single: 0 19 918788 6
  pack of 6: 0 19 918789 4

Blue Shoes
by Angela Bull; adapted by David Calcutt
  single: 0 19 918790 8
  pack of 6: 0 19 918791 6

Stage 13
The Personality Potion
by Alan MacDonald; adapted
by David Calcutt
  single: 0 19 918792 4
  pack of 6: 0 19 918793 2

Spooky!
by Michaela Morgan; adapted
by David Calcutt
  single: 0 19 918794 0
  pack of 6: 0 19 918795 9

Stage 14
Petey
by Paul Shipton; adapted
by David Calcutt
  single: 0 19 918796 7
  pack of 6: 0 19 918797 5

Climbing in the Dark
adapted from his own novel
by Nick Warburton
  single: 0 19 918798 3
  pack of 6: 0 19 918799 1